Zaner-Bloser
Handwriting

explore

D1378859

Zaner-Bloser
The Language Arts and Reading Company

Credits

Art: John Hovell: 85–87, 94

Literature: "This Land Is Your Land." Words and Music by Woody
Guthrie. TRO-© Copyright 1956 (Renewed), 1958 (Renewed) and 1970
Ludlow Music, Inc., New York, NY. Used by Permission.; "Arithmetic"
from THE COMPLETE POEMS OF CARL SANDBURG, copyright 1950
by Carl Sandburg and renewed 1978 by Margaret Sandburg, Helga
Sandburg Crile and Janet Sandburg, reproduced by permission of
Houghton Mifflin Harcourt Publishing Company.; "At the Library"
Copyright © 1997 by Nikki Grimes. First appeared in *It's Raining
Laughter* by Nikki Grimes, published by Dial Books for Young Readers.
Reprinted by permission of Curtis Brown, Ltd.; "When a City Leans
Against the Sky" by Allan De Fina, from *When a City Leans Against the
Sky*, ©1997 by Allan A. De Fina. Published by Wordsong, an imprint of
Boyds Mills Press. Reprinted by permission.

Photos: Photos: ©NASA/ESA/STScI/epa/Corbis: cover, title page;
©CORBIS: cover, title page; ©Images.com/Corbis: 4–5; ©George
Anderson Photography: 6; ©Peter Griffith/Getty Images: 7, 89;
©Terry Vine/Getty Images: 12–13; ©Juniors Bildarchiv/Photo Library:
15; ©Radius Images/Photo Library: 17; ©Hurewitz Creative/CORBIS:
18; ©Brasil2/iStockphoto: 21; ©Jon Feingersh Photography Inc./
Blend Images/Corbis: 24; ©Michael McCloskey/Getty Images: 27;

©Tschon/iStockphoto: 30; ©NASA-JPL: 33; ©Tom Uhlman/
Alamy: 38; ©Marcus Lindström/iStockphoto: 40; ©MIXA/Getty
Images: 42–43; ©Comstock/Corbis: 45; ©Sven Rosenhall/
Nordic Photos/PhotoLibrary: 46; ©Library of Congress - digital
ve/Science Faction/Corbis: 49; ©Walter Bibikow/JAI/Corbis:
51; ©Jupiterimages/Getty Images: 57, 81; ©The Gallery
Collection/Corbis: 58; ©age fotostock/SuperStock: 61; ©Jeremy
Woodhouse/Getty Images: 64; ©Mark Karrass/Corbis: 65;
©Paul Erickson/iStockphoto: 70; ©Yuji Gashida/amanaimages/
Corbis: 72–73; ©Chepko Danil/iStockphoto: 74 (top left);
©Aldo Murillo/iStockphoto: 74 (middle left); ©Steve Goodwin/
iStockphoto: 74 (bottom left); ©Monika Adamczyk/iStockphoto:
74 (top right); ©Ryan Lane/iStockphoto: 74 (middle right); ©Lisa
Thornberg/iStockphoto: 74 (bottom right); ©Frans Lanting/
Corbis: 82; ©Jerome Skiba/iStockphoto: 84; ©Mike Hargreaves/
FreshFoodImages/PhotoLibrary: 84; ©Hemera Technologies/Getty
Images: 84; ©Matthew Ward/Getty Images: 84; ©Tono Labra/
age fotostock/Photolibrary: 84; ©Laura Eisenberg/iStockphoto:
84; ©Ivan Bajic/iStockphoto: 84; ©National Geographic/Getty
Images: 84; ©Kasia Biel/iStockphoto: 84; ©ericsphotography/
iStockphoto: 92

ISBN 978-0-7367-6841-2   15 16 17 18 19 997   14 13 12 11 10

Zaner-Bloser, Inc.
1-800-421-3018
www.zaner-bloser.com
Printed in the United States of America

SUSTAINABLE FORESTRY INITIATIVE
Certified Chain of Custody
Promoting Sustainable Forestry
www.sfiprogram.org
SFI-00712

CONTENTS

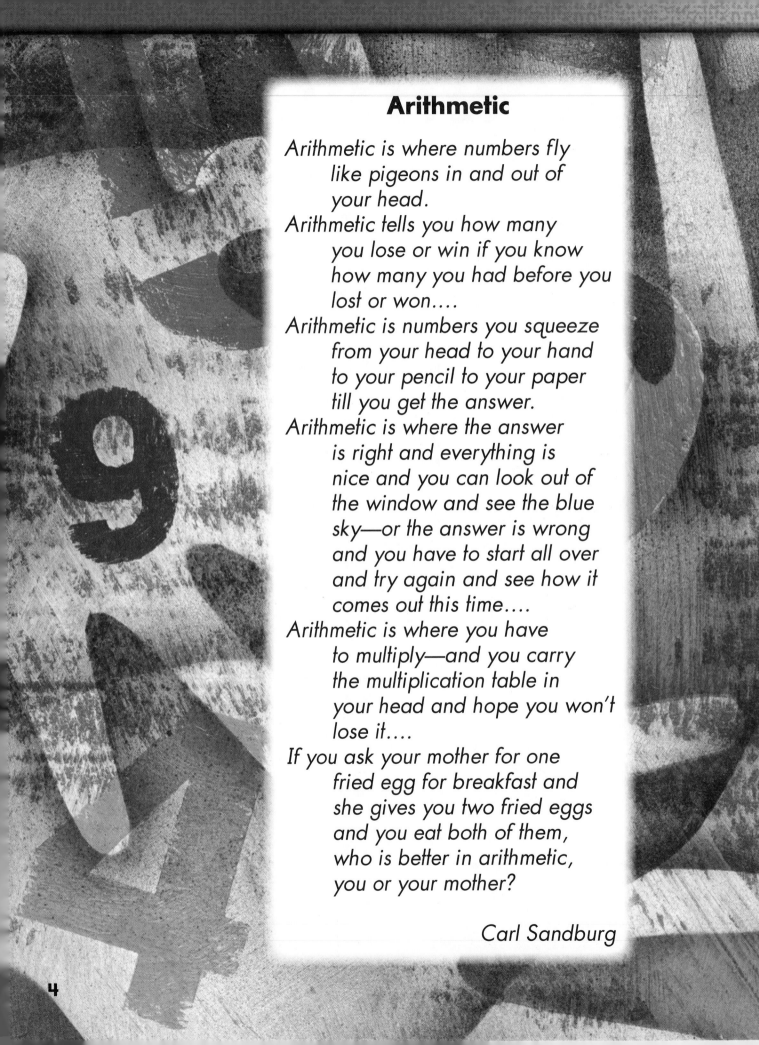

Arithmetic

Arithmetic is where numbers fly
    like pigeons in and out of
    your head.
Arithmetic tells you how many
    you lose or win if you know
    how many you had before you
    lost or won....
Arithmetic is numbers you squeeze
    from your head to your hand
    to your pencil to your paper
    till you get the answer.
Arithmetic is where the answer
    is right and everything is
    nice and you can look out of
    the window and see the blue
    sky—or the answer is wrong
    and you have to start all over
    and try again and see how it
    comes out this time....
Arithmetic is where you have
    to multiply—and you carry
    the multiplication table in
    your head and hope you won't
    lose it....
If you ask your mother for one
    fried egg for breakfast and
    she gives you two fried eggs
    and you eat both of them,
    who is better in arithmetic,
    you or your mother?

Carl Sandburg

A Frontier Tale

Lincoln Elementary Fifth Grade Play

Place: the Oregon wilderness, around 1845.

Act One

Scene One

Sarah Shaw (a pioneer): We've been traveling for months now, since the spring when we left Boston to come West.

Johnson (a trapper): It's a wide-open country, with plenty of land for everyone.

You write for many reasons at school, at home, and in your community. The lessons in this book will help you write legibly so you and other people can easily read what you have written.

Evaluating your own handwriting is a good habit to form. When you see the **Stop and Check** sign in this book, stop and circle the best letter you wrote on that line.

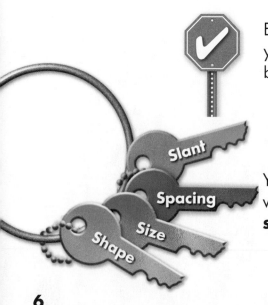

You will see the **Keys to Legibility** throughout this book. They will help you remember to check the **shape, size, spacing,** and **slant** of your writing to make sure it is easy to read.

On another piece of paper, write the first stanza of this American folk song in your best cursive handwriting.

Circle your three best letters. Underline three letters that need improvement.

This Land Is Your Land

This land is your land,
    this land is my land
From California to the New York
    island,
From the redwood forest to the
    Gulf Stream waters
This land was made
    for you and me.

As I was walking that ribbon
    of highway,
I saw above me that endless
    skyway,
I saw below me that golden
    valley
This land was made for you
    and me.

Woody Guthrie

7

Writing Positions and Basic Strokes

Sit comfortably with your feet flat on the floor.
Rest both arms on the desk. Shift your paper as you write.

Paper Position

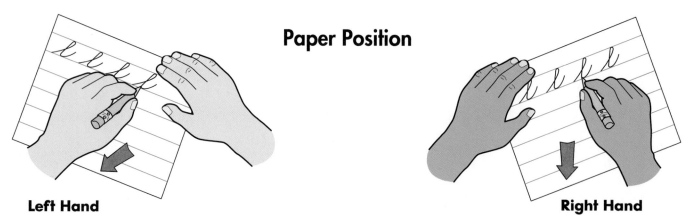

Left Hand

Right Hand

Pencil Position

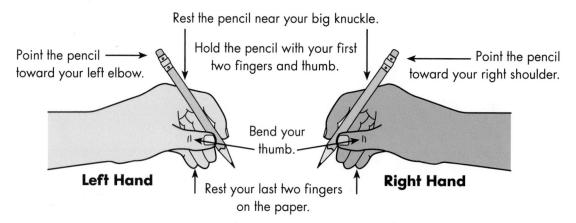

Rest the pencil near your big knuckle.

Point the pencil toward your left elbow.

Hold the pencil with your first two fingers and thumb.

Point the pencil toward your right shoulder.

Bend your thumb.

Left Hand

Rest your last two fingers on the paper.

Right Hand

Practice the basic cursive strokes.

Undercurve

Downcurve

Overcurve

Slant

Cursive Letters and Numerals

Aa Bb Cc Dd Ee Ff Gg
Hh Ii Jj Kk Ll Mm
Nn Oo Pp Qq Rr Ss Tt
Uu Vv Ww Xx Yy Zz
1 2 3 4 5 6 7 8 9 10

Write your full name.

_____

_____

Write the name of your school, its street address, and the city and state.

_____

_____

_____

_____

Write your date of birth and your age.

_____

_____

Write the title of your favorite book or song.

_____

_____

_____

Write the letters and numerals you like to write best.

_____

_____

_____

Shape

As you write in cursive, pay attention to the shape of your letters.
Using good basic strokes will improve the shape of your letters.

undercurve strokes	ı	t	S	j	w
downcurve strokes	c	g	a	o	c
overcurve strokes	c	v	y	n	f
slant strokes	ı	K	f	d	U

Size

You should also pay attention to the size of your writing.

Tall letters do not touch the headline.

Some lowercase letters are tall letters.	d	k	f	l
All uppercase letters are tall letters.	J	a	S	L
Numerals are the height of tall letters.	0	5	9	3

Short letters are half the height of tall letters.

Many lowercase letters are short letters.	c	v	m	a

Descenders do not go too far below the baseline.

Some lowercase letters have descenders.	g	p	z	j
Some uppercase letters have descenders.	J	Y	Z	

Spacing

Your spacing should be correct.

between letters

between words

between sentences

letters

word word

end Begin

Write the sentences below. Then check your spacing. Draw O between letters, \ between words, and O between sentences.

This spacing is correct. Shift your paper as you write.

Slant

The slant of your writing should be uniform.

All your letters should slant forward.

Check the slant. Draw lines through the slant strokes of the letters.

Are your lines parallel?

Write this sentence. Pay careful attention to shape, size, spacing, and slant.

This is my best handwriting.

At the Library

I flip the pages of a book and slip inside,
Where crystal seas await and pirates hide.
I find a paradise where birds can talk,
Where children fly and trees prefer to walk.
Sometimes I end up on a city street.
I recognize the brownskin girl I meet.
She's skinny, but she's strong, and brave, and wise.
I smile because I see me in her eyes.

Nikki Grimes

Write Undercurve Letters

Trace and write.

i   *i*   *i*   *i*   *i*   *i*   *i*   *i*   *i*   *i*

ie   *is*   *id*   *ic*   *in*   *im*

individual   *island*   *imagine*

icicles   *aliens*   *blister*

t   *t*   *t*   *t*   *t*   *t*   *t*   *t*   *t*   *t*

te   *ti*   *ta*   *to*   *ty*   *tm*

target   *tempt*   *tower*

activity   *department*   *notion*

Undercurve-to-Undercurve Joining

The undercurve ending swings wide directly into the
undercurve of the following letter.

ie **not** *ie*

✔ Check your writing folder for undercurve joinings
that need improvement.

Shape

Circle three
letters you wrote that
have good shape.

14

Trace and write.

u

u   u   u   u   u   u   u

ub   us   uo   ud   un   uv

universe   fluoride   cloudier

mustang   souvenir   ruby

w

w   w   w   w   w   w   w

we   wh   wa   wo   wn   wy

westward   wharf   wood

wardrobe   downhill   shadowy

Checkstroke-to-Undercurve Joining

The checkstroke ending (⌣) swings right to form the loop in *h*.

wh **not** *wh*

✔ Check your writing folder for checkstroke joinings that need improvement.

15

Write Undercurve Letters

Trace and write.

e

e   *e*   *e*   *e*   *e*   *e*   *e*   *e*

eb   *el*   *ed*   *ea*   *em*   *en*

earthen   *ebony*   *emerge*

delivery   *medium*   *keen*

l

l   *l*   *l*   *l*   *l*   *l*   *l*   *l*

ll   *lu*   *lo*   *la*   *ln*   *ly*

lullaby   *lower*   *lying*

mainland   *lumber*   *coolness*

Undercurve-to-Undercurve Joining

The undercurve joining must be wide to allow room
for the loop in *l*.

el **not** *el*

✔ Check your writing folder for undercurve joinings
that need improvement.

Size

Circle three
letters you wrote
that have good size.

Trace and write.

b

b   b   b   b   b   b   b   b

bi   br   bo   ba   by   bn

basic   broadcast   lobby

thumbnail   orbit   sunbonnet

h

h   h   h   h   h   h   h   h

he   hi   ho   ha   hy

heritage   hilltop   slushy

theory   shaky   shortcut

Checkstroke-to-Downcurve Joining

The checkstroke ending (⌣) swings right to form
the top of the downcurve letter.

bo **not** *bu*

✔ Check your writing folder for checkstroke joinings
that need improvement.

Clipped Words

Write the underlined part of each long word.
Then write the entire longer word.

1. _taxi_cab

2. _champ_ion

3. lun_ch_eon

4. tele_phone_

5. omni_bus_

6. news_paper_

7. _gym_nasium

8. _memo_randum

9. _exam_ination

10. _vet_erinarian

My writing has good Shape . ☐
My writing has good Size . ☐

Writing Legibly

I. **Study** these tips for legible writing. They will help you avoid common handwriting errors when you write.

✔ Keep loops open in letters with loops. Write *ℓ* not *ℓ*.

✔ Make sure your undercurves rest on the baseline. Write *u* not *u*.

✔ Keep checkstrokes at the right height. Write *b* not *b*.

✔ Keep your slant uniform. Write *w* not *w*.

2. **Look** at these words from a student's spelling list. Underline letters that need improvement.

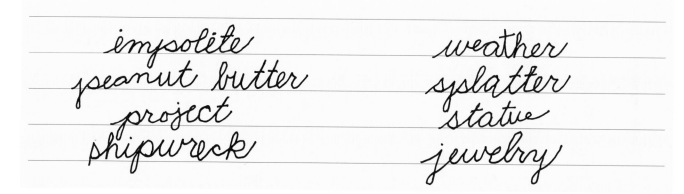

emsolete
peanut butter
project
shipwreck

weather
splatter
statue
jewelry

3. **Rewrite** the spelling words correctly; then write some of your spelling or vocabulary words. Remember to leave space for margins. Pay attention to the tips for legible writing.

Write Undercurve Letters

Trace and write.

f   f   f   f   f   f   f   f

fr   fi   fe   fa   fo   fy

fabric   firefighter   fowl

refrain   perfection   classify

k   k   k   k   k   k   k   k

ki   ks   ka   ko   kn   ky

karate   kilogram   knock

blacksmith   hickory   bulky

Undercurve-to-Overcurve Joining

The undercurve ending swings wide and then overcurves quickly into the slant stroke.

kn **not** *kn*

✔ Check your writing folder for undercurve joinings that need improvement.

Spacing

Circle your three best joinings.

20

Trace and write.

r   r   r   r   r   r   r   r

rf   ru   ri   ro   ra   ry

ranger   rugged   riverbed

underfoot   throng   pastry

s   s   s   s   s   s   s   s

st   sh   sc   sa   sn   sy

sandbar   scat   stagecoach

snappy   windshield   courtesy

Undercurve-to-Downcurve Joining

The undercurve swings wide and forms the top of the downcurve of the next letter.

ra **not** *ru*

✔ Check your writing folder for undercurve joinings that need improvement.

21

Write Undercurve Letters

j   *j*   *j*   *j*   *j*   *j*   *j*   *j* ✔

ju   *je*   *ji*   *ja*   *jo* ✔

jade   *journal*   *judgment*

jigsaw   *object*   *injury*

p   *p*   *p*   *p*   *p*   *p*   *p*   *p* ✔

ph   *pl*   *pe*   *pa*   *po*   *py* ✔

partial   *please*   *photograph*

people   *porpoise*   *choppy*

Overcurve-to-Undercurve Joining

The overcurve ending crosses at the baseline and turns into a wide undercurve.

ju **not** *ju*

✔ Check your writing folder for overcurve joinings that need improvement.

Slant

Circle three words you wrote that have good slant.

Compound Words

A compound word is made up of two words that come together to form a single word.
Fill in the missing letters in the puzzle to complete each compound word.
Use manuscript handwriting.

tumbleweeds	seaside	waterway
landform	farmhouse	newspaper
stagecoach	postmaster	northwestern

								w	e	e	d	s
												t
		n	e	w	s	_	_	_	_	_		a
		_										g
		_	f	a	r	m	_	_	_	_		e
		_										
		_										_
		w	_	_	_	_	w	a	y			_
		e										
p	o	s	t	_	_	_	_	_	_			_
		t										
	s	e	a	_	_	_	_					
		r										
_	_	n	_	f	o	r	m					

Review

Write Homophones

Write each sentence. Then circle two words that sound alike but have different spellings and meanings.

1. Use the oar, or you'll just float.

2. Jan ate all eight pieces of pizza.

3. The patients had much patience.

4. The crews worked on the cruise.

5. I read the red book while waiting.

6. What a cute pale blue pail!

7. Our math class lasts for an hour.

8. Some of us knew the sum.

9. Close the clothes closet door.

10. Sandpaper is coarse, of course!

My writing has good Shape ☐
My writing has good Size ☐
My writing has good Spacing ☐

Writing Legibly

I. Study these tips for legible writing. They will help you avoid common handwriting errors when you write.

- ✔ Make sure your letters slant forward. Write *f* not *f*.
- ✔ Retrace strokes in letters carefully. Write *s* not *s*.
- ✔ Make sure letters rest on the baseline. Write *v* not *v*.
- ✔ Remember to dot your letters. Write *j* not *j*.

2. Look at this section from a student's book review. Underline letters that need improvement.

> This book will leave you
> hungry for chocolate, jellybeans,
> and other treats. The main
> character of the book is Charlie,
> a smart boy from a poor family.
> He wins a ticket to tour a
> mysterious chocolate factory.

3. Rewrite the student's book review correctly; then write a book review of your own. Pay attention to the tips for legible writing. Remember to leave space for margins.

Write Downcurve Letters

Trace and write.

a   a   a   a   a   a   a   a   a

ab   as   ac   ad   am   an

absent   accept   adjective

amateur   arrange   reassure

d   d   d   d   d   d   d   d   d

di   de   du   da   dm   dy

data   development   diameter

eddy   landmark   reduce

Undercurve-to-Overcurve Joining

The undercurve ending swings wide and up to begin
the overcurve of the next letter.

am **not** am

✔ Check your writing folder for undercurve joinings
that need improvement.

Shape

Circle three
letters you wrote that
have good shape.

Trace and write.

g   *g*   *g*   *g*   *g*   *g*   *g*   *g*

ge   *gr*   *go*   *gg*   *gn*   *gy*

genius   *suggest*   *energy*

foreign   *vigorous*   *program*

o   *o*   *o*   *o*   *o*   *o*   *o*   *o*

ob   *ou*   *oa*   *od*   *on*   *ov*

oats   *observation*   *overreact*

onion   *courthouse*   *modem*

Overcurve-to-Downcurve Joining

The overcurve crosses at the baseline, then continues up and wide to form the top of the downcurve letter.

gg **not** *gy*

✔ Check your writing folder for overcurve joinings that need improvement.

Write Downcurve Letters

Trace and write.

c

c   c   c   c   c   c   c   c

ce   ch   ca   co   cy   cn

campaign   comment   picnic

machine   receive   democracy

q

q   q   q   q   q   q   q   q

qu   nq   iq   sq   eq   qu

quote   quart   quarry

conquer   unique   require

Undercurve-to-Undercurve Joining

The undercurve ending swings wide to begin the following letter.

qu **not** *qu*

✔ Check your writing folder for undercurve joinings that need improvement.

Size

Circle your three best tall letters.

Be a Wordsmith

A **wordsmith** is a person who works with words. Now it's your turn to be a wordsmith.
See how many words you can write using only the letters **w, o, r, d, s, m, i, t,** and **h**.
You may use each letter more than once. Write in manuscript.

wordsmith

The next word to try is **handwriting**.
See how many words you can write using the letters **h, a, n, d, w, r, i, t,** and **g**.
You may use each letter more than once. Write in manuscript.

handwriting

Review

Describing Words

The words in the box are adjectives that can be used to describe foods.

sour	salty	sticky	spicy
crunchy	sweet	juicy	crispy

Write an adjective to describe each food.

1. _____ cookies

2. _____ fries

3. _____ salsa

4. _____ chips

5. _____ oranges

6. _____ lemons

7. _____ syrup

8. _____ pretzels

Write about a snack you might prepare for your family. Use some of the adjectives you wrote above.

_____

_____

_____

_____

_____

_____

My writing has good Shape. ☐
My writing has good Size. ☐
My writing has good Spacing. ☐
My writing has good Slant. ☐

Writing Legibly

1. Study these tips for legible writing. They will help you avoid common handwriting errors when you write.

✔ Close letters that should be closed. Write *d* not *cl*.

✔ Keep checkstrokes at the right height. Write *o* not *a*.

✔ When letters have loops that go below the baseline, close the loop at the baseline. Write *g* not *g*.

2. Look at this part of a student's math story problem. Underline letters that need improvement.

> Ryan invited sixteen friends to a mid-week pizza party. Each pizza has eight slices. How many pizzas are needed so that the serving for each guest equals four slices?

3. Rewrite the math story problem correctly; then write a math story problem of your own. Remember to leave space for margins. Pay attention to the tips for legible writing.

Write Overcurve Letters

Trace and write.

n

n   n   n   n   n   n   n

ni   nu   no   na   nn   ny

naturalist   number   nightfall

noontime   announce   funny

m

m   m   m   m   m   m   m

mi   me   ma   mo   mn

mainland   mobile   menu

microscope   millimeter   autumn

Undercurve-to-Downcurve Joining

The undercurve swings up and over to form the top of the downcurve letter.

ma **not** ma

✔ Check your writing folder for undercurve joinings that need improvement.

Spacing

Circle your three best joinings.

Trace and write.

y

y   y   y   y   y   y   y ✔

ye   ys   yt   ya   yo   ym ✔

yard   yesterday   yoke

myth   physical   gymnast

x

x   x   x   x   x   x   x ✔

xp   xt   xi   xa   xc   xy ✔

expand   galaxy   texture

exist   exactly   exciting

Undercurve-to-Downcurve Joining

The undercurve swings up and over to form the top of the downcurve letter. Remember to cross your *x* after the word is finished.

xc **not** *xu*

✔ Check your writing folder for undercurve joinings that need improvement.

33

Write Overcurve Letters

Trace and write.

v *v* *v* *v* *v* *v* *v* *v*

ve *vi* *vo* *va* *vy*

vice president *vow* *value*

adventure *wavy* *arrive*

z *z* *z* *z* *z* *z* *z* *z*

ze *zi* *zo* *za* *zy* *zy*

zigzag *zone* *zaniest*

lazy *pretzel* *dizziness*

Overcurve-to-Overcurve Joining

The overcurve ending turns quickly into the overcurve stroke of the following letter.

zy **not** *zy*

✔ Check your writing folder for overcurve joinings that need improvement.

Slant

Circle three letters you wrote that have good slant.

Yearbook Entry

Your class is going to publish a yearbook.
Under each student's picture will be some information about that student.
Fill out the form below for your entry in the yearbook. Write in manuscript.

First Name:

Grade:

School:

Favorite subject:

Favorite sport or hobby:

What I like best about school:

What I like to do after school:

Favorite book:

Favorite movie:

Undercurve Ending

Before you join one letter to another, look at the way the letter ends.

Letters *i*, *e*, *t*, *l*, and *s* end with an undercurve. Look at the ways they may be joined to other letters.

Undercurve-to-Undercurve Joining *lu*

Trace and write the undercurve-to-undercurve joinings.
Then write the words.

ef   ib   lk   se

di   tr   ce   qu   fit   deep   hulk

Undercurve-to-Downcurve Joining *ta*

Trace and write the undercurve-to-downcurve joinings.
Then write the words.

ea   sc   rd   ug

ma   nd   ig   lo   tag   no   pad

Undercurve-to-Overcurve Joining *sy*

Trace and write the undercurve-to-overcurve joinings.
Then write the words.

im   ry   sn   fy

ay   mm   un   hy   sum   ax   day

Read the sentence and circle joinings in which the first letter ends in an undercurve. Then rewrite the sentence.

Sam plays baseball every spring.

Overcurve Ending

Letters *j*, *y*, *g*, and *z* end with an overcurve. Look at the ways they may be joined to other letters.

Overcurve-to-Undercurve Joining *ju*

Trace and write the overcurve-to-undercurve joinings. Then write the words.

jb   ye   gu   zi

ge   yr   zw   jk   jug   zipper   yes

Overcurve-to-Downcurve Joining *ga*

Trace and write the overcurve-to-downcurve joinings. Then write the words.

ja   zo   yd   ga

yo   jc   zd   gd   go   jam   yo-yo

Overcurve-to-Overcurve Joining *zy*

Trace and write the overcurve-to-overcurve joinings. Then write the words.

gn   zy   jy   yv

zn   ym   jv   gv   gnome   lazy   symphony

Read the sentence and circle joinings in which the first letter ends in an overcurve. Then rewrite the sentence.

The judges liked the gymnast who won
a medal last year.

Alliterative Phrases

The words in each phrase below begin with the same sound. This is called alliteration.

yak-yak

perfectly plain pasta

zigzagging zebras

neat notebook notes

velvety voices

mysterious meandering maze

Write a sentence to answer each question. Use an alliterative phrase.

1. What animal talks too much?

2. What is easy to read?

3. Where might you get lost?

4. What is spaghetti with no sauce?

5. What are black and white inline skaters?

6. What does a smooth-sounding singing group have?

My writing has good *Shape* . ☐
My writing has good *Size* . ☐
My writing has good *Spacing* . ☐
My writing has good *Slant* . ☐

Writing Legibly

1. Study these tips for legible writing. They will help you avoid common handwriting errors when you write.

✔ When letters have loops that go below the baseline, close the loop at the baseline. Write _y_ not _y_.

✔ Keep checkstrokes at the right height. Write _v_ not _u_.

✔ Make sure curves are smooth and rounded. Write _m_ not _m_.

✔ Begin overcurve letters with an overcurve. Write _x_ not _x_.

2. Look at this part of a student's health report. Underline letters that need improvement.

> Eating balanced meals is one way
> to keep healthy. Some people take
> extra vitamins and enzymes for
> added nutrition. Regular exercise
> is also important.

3. Rewrite the report correctly; then write part of a report you have written. Pay attention to the tips for legible writing. Remember to leave space for margins.

Slant

Spacing

Size

Shape

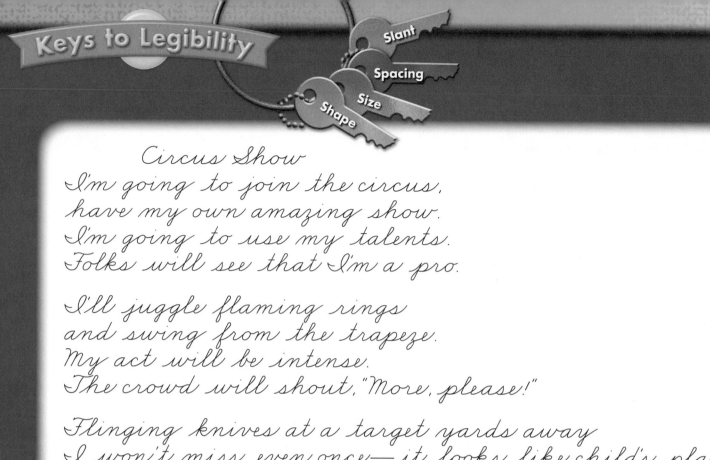

Circus Show

I'm going to join the circus,
have my own amazing show.
I'm going to use my talents.
Folks will see that I'm a pro.

I'll juggle flaming rings
and swing from the trapeze.
My act will be intense.
The crowd will shout, "More, please!"

Flinging knives at a target yards away
I won't miss even once—it looks like child's play!
And when I heave and lift five hundred pounds,
the audience will make loud, gasping sounds.

Then I'll put on my wig, big shoes, and red nose,
jump up, fall down, strike a hilarious pose.
But the best part of my act is its ending,
for a smiling crowd to their homes I'm sending.

Write the poem. Make your writing easy to read. Be sure to leave space for margins.

Is your writing easy to read?

Shape
Circle your best letter that has an overcurve beginning.

Size
Circle your best tall letter.

Spacing
Circle two words that have space for \ between them.

Slant
Circle a word you wrote that has good slant.

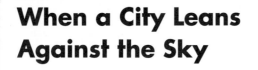

When a City Leans Against the Sky

*When a city
leans against the sky,
buildings squeeze and
press for elbowroom
with the clouds.
The sky turns blue
and bursts into sun
or moon and stars.*

Allan A. De Fina

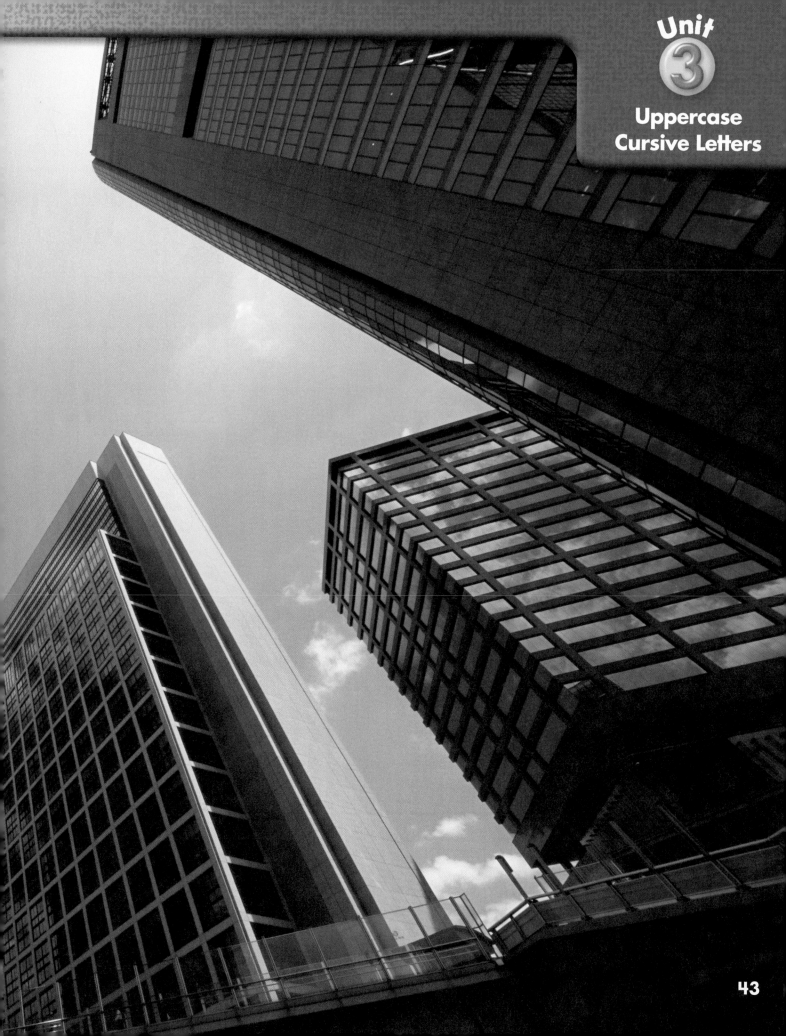

Write Downcurve Letters

Trace and write.

a

a a a a a a a a a ✓

Al Ap Ad Ag An Am ✓

Alamo Adirondacks America

Anasazi Appalachia Andover

O

O o o o o o o o O ✓

Oklahoma Oregon Omaha

Orlando Ocean City Oakland

Did You Know?

Akron is a city in Ohio.

Joining Alert

a is joined to the letter that follows.
O is not joined to the letter that follows.

Ad **not** Od

The undercurve-to-downcurve joining becomes a doublecurve. At the end of the doublecurve, you retrace.

Shape

Circle your three best uppercase letters that have a downcurve beginning.

44

Trace and write.

D

𝒟   𝒟   𝒟   𝒟   𝒟   𝒟   𝒟   𝒟

Dallas   Des Moines   Dover

Dodge City   Douglas   Davis

C

C   C   C   C   C   C   C   C

Ce   Ch   Ci   Ca   Co   Cy

Catskills   Chicago   Cypress

E

E   E   E   E   E   E   E   E

Er   El   Ea   Ed   En   Em

Elk City   East   Emmy

Joining Alert

𝒟 is not joined to the letter that follows.

C and E are joined to the letter that follows.

En **not** En

The undercurve swings wide and then overcurves quickly into the slant stroke of the next letter.

Write these facts about oceans.

1. The Earth has four oceans.

2. Oceans cover about 70 percent of Earth.

3. Climates are affected by oceans.

4. Earth's oceans flow into one another.

5. Many ships sail the Atlantic Ocean.

6. Deepest of the four is the Pacific.

7. The Arctic is the smallest ocean.

8. The Indian Ocean touches four of Earth's continents.

BONUS

Can you name the four continents that touch the Indian Ocean?

My writing has good  Shape. ☐
My writing has good Size. ☐
My writing has good Spacing. ☐
My writing has good Slant. ☐

Writing Legibly

1. Study these tips for legible writing. They will help you avoid common handwriting errors when you write.

✔ Close letters that should be closed. Write $\mathcal{a}$ not $\mathcal{u}$.

✔ Write strokes carefully. Write $\mathcal{D}$ not $\mathcal{D}$.

✔ Make sure curves are smooth and rounded. Write $\mathcal{E}$ not $\mathcal{E}$.

✔ Make sure all uppercase letters are tall. Write $\mathcal{C}$ not $\mathcal{C}$.

2. Look at this section from a student's geography report. Underline letters that need improvement.

> colombia is the only South American country with coastlines on both the North Pacific Ocean and the Caribbean Sea. The Andes mountain range runs through Colombia and continues south to Ecuador. The Guajira Desert is in the northernmost part of colombia.

3. Rewrite the student's geography report correctly, then choose a country and write a report of your own. Pay attention to the tips for legible writing. Remember to leave space for margins.

Write Curve Forward Letters

Trace and write.

n   n   n   n   n   n   n   n

Ne   Ni   Nu   Na   No   Ny

New Jersey   North Dakota

Nashville   New Orleans   Nome

m   m   m   m   m   m   m   m

Mi   Mu   Me   Mo   Ma   My

Montana   Minnesota   Missouri

Maryland   Myrtle Beach

Joining Alert

N and M are joined to the letter that follows.

Ne **not** Ne   Me **not** Me

The undercurve joining must be wide enough to allow room for the loop in e.

Size

Circle your three best tall letters.

48

Trace and write.

H   H   H   H   H   H   H   H

Hi   He   Hu   Ha   Ho   Hy

Harlem   Houston   Hiram

Hancock   High Plains   Hamilton

K   K   K   K   K   K   K   K

Ki   Ke   Ka   Ko   Kn   Ky

Kansas   Kentucky   Kitty Hawk

Key West   Knoxville   Kokomo

Joining Alert

H and K are joined to the letter that follows.

He   not   He

The loop swings across the letter and slightly down to make room for the loop in e.

49

Write Curve Forward Letters

Trace and write.

U U U U U U U U U

Ut Ur Ua Ug Um Un

The United States   Utah

The United Nations   Urbana

Y Y Y Y Y Y Y Y Y

Ye Yi Yu Yo Ya

Youngstown Yorktown Yukon

Yosemite Yellowstone Yuma

Joining Alert

U and Y are joined to the letter that follows.

Ya **not** Ya

The overcurve ending crosses at the baseline and then continues up and wide to form the downcurve letter.

Spacing

Circle three words you wrote that have good joinings.

Trace and write.

Z Z Z Z Z Z Z Z

Zu Ze Zh Za Zo Zy

Zanesville Zurich Zuni

New Zealand Zion National Park

V V V V V V V V

Vallejo Virginia Vermont

Vicksburg Valley Forge Vista

Did You Know?

Mount Vernon is in Virginia.

Joining Alert

Z is joined to the letter that follows.

V is not joined to the letter that follows.

Zo **not** Zo

The overcurve ending crosses at the baseline and then continues up and wide to form the downcurve letter.

51

Write Curve Forward Letters

Trace and write.

W   W   W   W   W   W   W   W

West Virginia   Washington

Mt. Whitney   Williamsburg

X   X   X   X   X   X   X   X

Xenia   Xanthus   Xenon

Xalapa, Mexico   Xapuri, Brazil

Did You Know?

Washington is a West-Coast state.

Joining Alert

W is not joined to the letter that follows.
Joining X is optional.

Xe   Xe

Unjoined   **Joined**

Size

Circle your three best tall letters.

52

A Number Code

1	2	3	4	5	6	7	8	9	10	11	12	13
A	B	C	D	E	F	G	H	I	J	K	L	M

14	15	16	17	18	19	20	21	22	23	24	25	26
N	O	P	Q	R	S	T	U	V	W	X	Y	Z

Each number in the code stands for a letter.
Decode each riddle and its answer. Write in uppercase manuscript.

23   8   1   20   4   15   5   19

?

4   5   12   1   23   1   18   5

!

1   14   5   23   10   5   18   19   5   25

23   8   5   18   5   8   1   19

?

15   18   5   7   15   14

!

20   15   15   11   12   1   8   15   13   1

Write your own message using the code.

Names of States

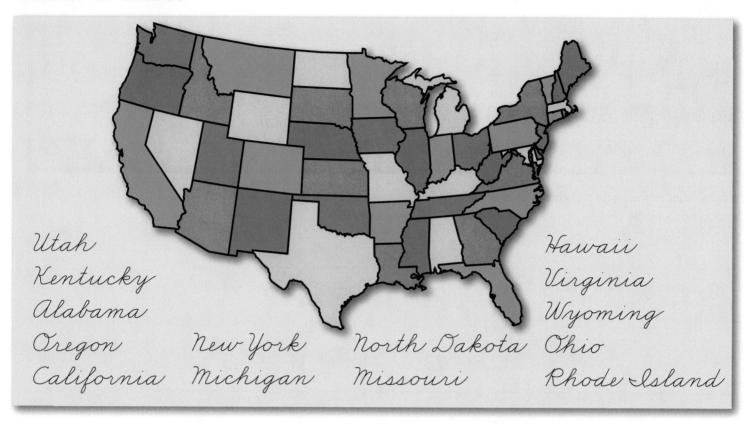

Utah
Kentucky
Alabama
Oregon
California

New York
Michigan

North Dakota
Missouri

Hawaii
Virginia
Wyoming
Ohio
Rhode Island

Write these names of states under the correct heading. Use your best cursive handwriting.

Names with fewer than 8 letters

_____

_____

_____

_____

_____

_____

Names with 8 letters or more

_____

_____

_____

_____

_____

_____

BONUS

Which state is known as the "Show-Me State"?

My writing has good ● Shape . ☐
My writing has good ● Size . ☐
My writing has good ● Spacing . ☐
My writing has good ● Slant . ☐

Writing Legibly

I. Study these tips for legible writing. They will help you avoid common handwriting errors when you write.

✔ Write strokes carefully. Write K not K.

✔ Don't add loops to letters that should not be looped. Write n not n.

✔ Make sure all uppercase letters are tall. Write M not m.

2. Look at this section from a student's history paper. Underline letters that need improvement.

> Are you curious about faraway galaxies? In 1803, Thomas Jefferson was curious about the unexplored West. He asked Meriwether Lewis and William Clark to go and learn all they could about the land between the Mississippi River and the Pacific Ocean.

3. Rewrite the student's paper correctly, or write a section from one of your own papers. Pay attention to the tips for legible writing. Remember to leave space for margins.

Write Overcurve Letters

Trace and write.

I   *I*   *I*   *I*   *I*   *I*   *I*   *I*   *I*   *I*

Indiana   *Idaho*   *Illinois*

J   *J*   *J*   *J*   *J*   *J*   *J*   *J*   *J*   *J*

Ji   *Je*   *Ju*   *Jo*   *Ja*   *Jy*

Jackson   *Jamestown*   *Juneau*

Q   *Q*   *Q*   *Q*   *Q*   *Q*   *Q*   *Q*   *Q*   *Q*

Quanah   *Quakertown*   *Quimby*

Did You Know?

Quanah is a city in Texas.

Joining Alert

J is joined to the letter that follows.

Q is not joined to the letter that follows.

Joining *I* is optional.

In   *In*

Unjoined   **Joined**

Shape

Circle three letters you wrote that have good shape.

Write Doublecurve Letters

Trace and write.

T   T   T   T   T   T   T   T   T

Tallahassee   Texas   Tetons

Lake Tahoe   Tucson   Tacoma

F   F   F   F   F   F   F   F

Fairfax   Fort Sumter   Fulton

Franklin   Fitchburg   Flagstaff

Did You Know?

The Everglades are in Florida.

Florida and Texas are in the South.

Joining Alert

Joining T and F is optional.

Ty   Fa   Ty   Fa

Unjoined   **Joined**

Review

U.S. Presidents

Write the names of the first ten presidents of the United States.

1. George Washington

2. John Adams

3. Thomas Jefferson

4. James Madison

5. James Monroe

6. John Quincy Adams

7. Andrew Jackson

8. Martin Van Buren

9. William Henry Harrison

10. John Tyler

BONUS

How many U.S. presidents have the name "John"?

My writing has good **Shape**. ❏
My writing has good **Size**. ❏
My writing has good **Spacing**. ❏
My writing has good **Slant**. ❏

Writing Legibly

I. Study these tips for legible writing. They will help you avoid common handwriting errors when you write.

✔ Keep loops open in letters with loops. Write *ℓ* not *ℓ*.

✔ When letters have loops that go below the baseline, close the loop at the baseline. Write *g* not *g*.

✔ Make sure your letters rest on the baseline. Write *Q* not *Q*.

✔ Keep your slant uniform. Write *T* not *T*.

2. Look at this speech from a student running for student council. Underline letters that need improvement.

> As president of Student Council, I, Joe Smith, promise to get the job done right. My motto is "Qualified, Trustworthy, and Fair," because I have the knowledge and experience needed for this position. Thank you for your vote!

3. Rewrite the speech correctly. Then imagine you are running for student council, and write a speech of your own. Pay attention to the tips for legible writing. Remember to leave space for margins.

Stop and Check
Circle your best letter.

Write Undercurve-Loop Letters

Trace and write.

G   G   G   G   G   G   G   G

Gettysburg   Grayling   Gary

Golden   Gibraltar   Gallup

S   S   S   S   S   S   S   S

South Dakota   South Carolina

Salem   Savannah   Seattle

L   L   L   L   L   L   L   L

Lafayette   Louisiana   Lansing

Lake Erie   Lexington   Lima

Joining Alert

L is not joined to the letter that follows.
Joining G and S is optional.

Go Sa   Go Sa

Unjoined   **Joined**

Size

Circle three letters you wrote that have good size.

Write Undercurve-Slant Letters

Trace and write.

P   P   P   P   P   P   P   P   P

Pennsylvania   Philadelphia

Palo Alto   The Pacific Palisades

R   R   R   R   R   R   R   R   R

Rh   Re   Ri   Ra   Ro   Ry

Raleigh   Rhode Island   Reno

B   B   B   B   B   B   B   B   B

Boston   Boise   Bunker Hill

Boonesville   Bowie   Buffalo

R is joined to the letter that follows.
P is not joined to the letter that follows.
Joining B is optional.

Ba   Ba

Unjoined   **Joined**

Write the words.

Joining *a*, *c*, and *ε*

The letters *a*, *c*, and *ε* are joined to the letter that follows. The undercurve swings to form the first stroke of the next letter. The undercurve must be wide enough to allow room for joining to the next letter.

Apple   *Crying*   *Elk*   *Eating*

 **Joining Alert**

Cursive letters *O* and *D* are not joined to the letter that follows.

Joining *n* and *m*

The letters *n* and *m* are joined to the letter that follows. The undercurve must be wide enough to allow room for joining to the next letter.

Need   *Nurse*   *Mama*   *Mouse*

Joining *H* and *K*

The letters *H* and *K* are joined to the letter that follows. The loop in *H* swings across the letter and slightly down to allow room for joining to the next letter.

Hard   *Hold*   *Kirk*   *Kurt*

Joining *U*, *Y*, and *Z*

The letters *U*, *Y*, and *Z* are joined to the letter that follows. The overcurve ending in *Y* and *Z* crosses at the baseline and then continues up and wide to form the downcurve letter.

Upon　　　　*Yard*　　　　*Yield*　　　　*Zoo*

Cursive letters *V* and *W* are not joined to the letter that follows.
Joining *X* is optional.

Joining *I*

The letter *I* is joined to the letter that follows. The slant stroke closes the top loop in *I* near the baseline before the letter loops back. It ends with an overcurve to join to the next letter.

Jacob　　　*Jillian*　　　*Jordan*　　　*June*

Cursive letters *Q* and *L* are not joined to the letter that follows.
Joining *I*, *T*, *F*, *G*, and *S* to the letter that follows is optional.

Joining *R*

The letter *R* is joined to the letter that follows. The undercurve joining must be wide enough to allow room for joining to the next letter.

Riverside　　*Roanoke*　　*Raven*　　*Ryan*

Cursive letter *P* is not joined to the letter that follows.
Joining cursive letter *B* to the letter that follows is optional.

✓ Stop and Check
Circle your best letter.

National Parks

Rocky Mountain, Colorado
Bryce Canyon, Utah
Glacier, Montana
Lake Clark, Alaska
Shenandoah, Virginia
Sequoia, California
Redwood, California
Petrified Forest, Arizona
Grand Canyon, Arizona
Big Bend, Texas

Write the names of national parks you can visit in each of these states.

Texas _____

Colorado _____

_____

Montana _____

Virginia _____

_____

California _____

Utah _____

_____

Alaska _____

Arizona _____

_____

_____

My writing has good Shape. ☐
My writing has good Size. ☐
My writing has good Spacing. ☐
My writing has good Slant. ☐

Writing Legibly

When you edit and proofread your writing, do you remember to check your handwriting? Taking time to make sure your handwriting is legible shows courtesy to your readers. It also helps you keep your handwriting skills sharp. Follow these steps for writing legibly.

I. Study tips for legible writing. The Keys to Legibility are easy to remember. They tell you what qualities to look for in your handwriting.

✔ Each letter should have good **Shape**.

Write *b* **not** *b*. Write *e* **not** *e*.

✔ Make sure letters are the proper **Size**. Tall letters should be twice the height of short letters.

Write *Adam* **not** *Adam*.

✔ Check for good **Spacing**. Leave space for ◯ between letters, space for \ between words, and space for ◯ between sentences.

Write *Check the chalkboard* not

Check the chalkboard.

✔ Keep your **Slant** uniform.

Write *f* **not** *f*.

2. Look closely at your handwriting. Underline places that need improvement in this student's story beginning.

A rainy day found my cousin Robin and me stuck inside at our aunt's house. We got bored just hanging around playing video games. "Let's explore the basement of this old house," Robin said. I agreed. Down the damp, crumbling steps we went, brushing cobwebs from our faces. Thick dust lay over boxes, jars, and strange artifacts stacked on leaning shelves.

"Hey, what's this?" Robin shouted, making my shoulders shake with fright.

"It looks like a door," I said as I knelt to open the rotting square of wood on rusty hinges.

"It's some kind of passageway," Robin guessed. "Let's check it out."

3. Rewrite the student's story beginning in your own handwriting. Use your best cursive handwriting.

Stop and Check
Circle your best letter.

Cursive Review

Write each joining. Then write two words that contain the joining. Use the dictionary to help you find words.

undercurve-to-undercurve	*us*	
undercurve-to-downcurve	*ed*	
undercurve-to-overcurve	*my*	
overcurve-to-undercurve	*ju*	
overcurve-to-downcurve	*yo*	
overcurve-to-overcurve	*zy*	
checkstroke-to-undercurve	*br*	
checkstroke-to-downcurve	*wa*	
checkstroke-to-overcurve	*by*	

Now write four sentences using some of the words you wrote above. Remember to leave space for margins.

a, C, E, N, M, H, K, U, Y, Z, J, and *R* are joined to the letter that follows.

O, D, V, W, Q, L, and *P* are not joined to the letter that follows.

Joining *X, I, T, F, G, S,* and *B* to the letter that follows is optional.

Play Geography

Write a list of place names. Each place name must begin with the last letter of the previous name.
The list is started for you. Remember to leave space for margins.

Mississippi, Indiana, Akron,
Nome, Evanston,

Yosemite National Park is one of California's most beautiful landmarks. Its greatest attraction is a large rock formation called Half Dome. Rock climbers go up the face of the rock, while hikers take the Mist Trail. The trail winds past Vernal Falls and Nevada Falls before it gets steeper and more challenging.

Write the paragraph about Yosemite National Park. Make your writing easy to read. Remember to leave space for margins.

Is your writing easy to read?

Shape
Circle your best letter that begins with a curve forward stroke.

Size
Circle your best uppercase letter.

Spacing
Circle two sentences that have space for O between them.

Slant
Circle a word you wrote that has good slant.

Who Has Seen the Wind?

Who has seen the wind?
Neither I nor you.
But when the leaves hang trembling,
The wind is passing through.
Who has seen the wind?
Neither you nor I.
But when the trees bow down their heads,
The wind is passing by.

Christina Rossetti

Using Your Writing

Now that you have practiced writing letters, you are ready to write without models.
You'll find that the more you write in cursive, the easier and faster it will be. In the following lessons,
you'll write more and learn more about how to make your writing easy to read.

Write at least two sentences that send a holiday message to a friend.

Happy Holiday!

Write Research Questions

Writing research questions helps you narrow a topic and find the facts you need. Choose a state that you would like to research. Read the example questions about Michigan. Then, in the space below, write at least six research questions about the state you chose.

Michigan
1. Where in the United States is it located?
2. What is the state capital?
3. What does the state flag look like?
4. What is the weather like?
5. What does the state manufacture?
6. What are the most populated cities?

Do your letters have good shape? Yes No
Is your writing easy to read? Yes No

Write Titles

Underline the titles of long works, including books, magazines, newspapers, movies, and Web sites.

Books	Journeys in Time	Movies	The Patriot
Magazines	U.S. News and World Report	Web sites	www.highlightskids.com
Newspapers	The New York Times		

Use quotation marks around the titles of short works, including short stories, articles, and songs.

Short Stories	"The Story of Lewis and Clark"	Songs	"America the Beautiful"
Articles	"Florida's Great Natural Wonders"		

Rewrite the following titles. Add an underline or quotation marks to each title.

(book)   *Places in Time*

(magazine)   *Cobblestone*

(movie)   *California, Here I Come!*

(article)   *The Story of the Oregon Trail*

(song)   *The Star-Spangled Banner*

(story)   *The Open Window*

(Web site)   *www.highlights.com*

(newspaper)   *International Herald Tribune*

Write a Business Letter

Read this business letter. Notice its six parts.

541 Lake Drive
Round Rock, Texas 78664
October 7, _____ ← heading

Washington Board of Tourism
12 Main Street, Suite 5C
Port Townsend, Washington 98368 ← inside address

Dear Tourism Director: ← greeting

I am interested in facts about Washington's population, geography, and history. Please send me any free information you offer. ← body

Thank you very much.
Sincerely, ← closing
Lee Hsu ← signature

Write the body of this letter in cursive, paying attention to the size and shape of your letters.

_____

_____

_____

_____

Remember that tall letters should not touch the headline.

Do your tall letters avoid touching the headline?   Yes   No
Is your writing legible?   Yes   No

Write Notes

When you take notes from an article or book, first write the title and the author.
Then write the most important facts in your own words.

Read the following passage about Florida and the notes a student wrote about it. Then write more notes about the passage in cursive handwriting. As you write, pay attention to the shape and size of your letters.

Florida's History by William Wycher

Florida has an exciting history. Juan Ponce de León, a Spanish explorer, first arrived there in 1513 in search of a mythical "fountain of youth." He didn't find the fountain, but he did find lots of flowers. The word "florida" is Spanish for "many flowers." Florida was not settled until 1565, when the Spanish founded St. Augustine. This city would become the United States' first permanent European settlement. In 1763, Spain traded Florida to the English. England ruled Florida until 1784, when Spain took it back. In 1821, the United States took control of Florida. Florida became a state in 1845. It has been nicknamed the "Sunshine State."

"Florida's History" by William Wycher

1. Ponce de León arrives in 1513 in search of "fountain of youth."

2. The word "florida" means "many flowers" in Spanish.

3.

4.

| | Do your letters have good shape? | Yes | No |
| Shape | Is your writing easy to read? | Yes | No |

Write an Outline

An outline is a writing plan. Here is the first part of an outline for a report on the state of Virginia.

All About "Old Dominion," the State of Virginia ← title
   I. *Virginia's History* ← main topic
      A. *First Settlers* ← subtopic
         1. *Iroquoian and Algonquian Indians* ← detail
         2. *English settlers at Jamestown, 1607* ← detail
      B. *American Revolution* ← subtopic

Use the details below to complete the outline. Pay attention to the shape and size of your letters.

Shenandoah National Park   President George Washington   Meriwether Lewis

Jefferson's home at Monticello   President Thomas Jefferson   William Clark

II. *Virginia's Tourist Attractions*

    A. *National Parks* _____

        1. Jamestown Festival Park _____

        2. _____

    B. *General Attractions* _____

        1. Colonial Williamsburg _____

        2. _____

III. *Famous Virginians*

    A. *Explorers* _____

        1. _____

        2. _____

    B. *Leaders* _____

        1. _____

        2. _____

Size

Are your tall letters the same size?	Yes	No
Do your descenders avoid crashing into the letters below?	Yes	No

Write a Paragraph

A paragraph is a group of sentences related to a main idea. The following sentences make up a paragraph. Notice that the first line is indented.

> *Many famous people come from Virginia, especially explorers and politicians. For example, explorers Meriwether Lewis and William Clark were born in Virginia. George Washington and Thomas Jefferson, two United States presidents, were also born in Virginia.*

Rewrite the paragraph using your best cursive handwriting. Pay attention to the shape and size of your letters.

Did You Know?

Richmond is the capital of Virginia.

Shape

Do your letters have good shape?   Yes   No
Is your writing easy to read?   Yes   No

Write Greetings

Every language has words used to greet people.

	Hello	Good-bye
French	bonjour	au revoir
Spanish	hola	hasta la vista
German	guten Tag	auf wiedersehen
Italian	buon giorno	ciao
Swahili	jambo	kwahire
Chinese	nei ho	joi gin
Turkish	merhaba	güle güle

1. Write **hello** and **good-bye** in Spanish. Use your best cursive handwriting.

2. Write **hello** and **good-bye** in Italian. Use your best cursive handwriting.

3. Write **hello** and **good-bye** in French. Use your best cursive handwriting.

4. Write **hello** and **good-bye** in Swahili. Use your best cursive handwriting.

5. Write **hello** and **good-bye** in Chinese. Use your best cursive handwriting.

Write your family's favorite way to say **hello** and **good-bye**. Use your best cursive handwriting.

Spacing

Is the spacing between your letters correct?	Yes No
Is your writing easy to read?	Yes No

Write a List

Lists help to organize important ideas.
Here is a list of endangered species and where they live.

Species	Areas
giant armadillo	Venezuela, from Guyana to Argentina
Mexican bobcat	Central Mexico
American crocodile	U.S., Mexico, Caribbean Sea, Central and South America
Asian elephant	South central and southeastern Asia
gorilla	Central and West Africa
kangaroo	Australia
lion	Africa, India
orangutan	Borneo, Sumatra

Choose four species you would like to help save.
List the species and the countries in which they live. Use your best cursive handwriting.

1. _____

_____

2. _____

_____

3. _____

_____

4. _____

_____

Spacing

| Did you use correct spacing between your words? | Yes | No |
| Is your writing easy to read? | Yes | No |

Write a Poem

Many people write poems for fun and to learn more about themselves.
Write a poem about yourself by answering each of the questions below. Use your best cursive handwriting.

A "Me" Poem

Line 1.   Your first name only

Line 2.   Who likes (3 words)

Line 3.   Who does not like (3 words)

Line 4.   Who is good at (3 words)

Line 5.   Who spends time (3 words)

Line 6.   Who wants to learn (3 words)

Line 7.   Who wants to be (3 words)

Line 8.   Your last name only

Is the spacing between your letters correct?	Yes	No
Is your writing easy to read?	Yes	No

Write Labels

cowrie shell

sundial

sea urchin

sand dollar

scallop

oyster

bubble shell

landsnail

spindle shell

precious wentletrap

Unscramble the name of each shell in the collection.
Write each label in your best manuscript.

esa churin

sdleinp ehsll

sdunail

locsalp

sdalnnial

bbbleu ellsh

oreyts

dsan lolard

cweior llesh

erpousic wepratnlet

The Writing Process
Write a Story

A short story is a brief work of fiction that contains made-up characters and events.
A story takes place at a specific time and place, called the **setting**.
The action is based around a series of events, called the **plot**.

Here are some possible ideas for your story.

> **Imagine you are taking a trip.**
> **Write a story about all the things that happen on your trip.**
>
> **Imagine that you dig up a mysterious trunk.**
> **Write a story about the things you find in that trunk.**

Follow these steps for writing a short story.

I. Prewriting
Start by thinking about a plot for your short story. **Plan** your plot using the chart below.
Write legibly so you can read your ideas later. Use your best cursive handwriting.

Setting:

Characters:

Problem:

Events:

Solution:

2. Drafting
Write your first draft.

Make sure that your tall letters do not bump into descenders above them.

My writing has good **Shape** . ❑
My writing has good **Size** . ❑
My writing has good **Spacing** . ❑
My writing has good **Slant** . ❑

3. Revising

Read your draft and mark any changes you want to make. You might want to ask a classmate to help you. Use editing marks as you revise your short story.

Use these proofreading marks to edit your writing.

☰	Capitalize	∧	Insert or add
/	Use lowercase	ℛ	Delete or take out
⊙	Add a period	¶	Indent for a new paragraph

4. Editing

Check your story for errors in spelling, punctuation, capitalization, and handwriting. Answer the questions below to help you edit your story. You might want to ask a classmate to help you.

Is your story interesting?	Yes	No
Does the ending make sense?	Yes	No
Does your story include dialogue?	Yes	No
Are all the words spelled correctly?	Yes	No
Did you avoid collisions?	Yes	No
Do your letters rest on the baseline?	Yes	No
Are your short letters half the height of your tall letters?	Yes	No
Is there good spacing between your letters, words, and sentences?	Yes	No
Does your writing have uniform slant?	Yes	No
Is your writing legible?	Yes	No

5. Publishing

In your best cursive handwriting, make a clean copy of your story.
Then follow these steps to publish your story:

• Add a title and your name.

• Add an illustration, if you wish.

• Read your story to a small group of classmates.

Manuscript Maintenance
A Homework Plan

Make a homework plan for next week. Write the information in the sample, or make up a plan of your own. Use manuscript writing.

Day	Subject	Time	Materials
Monday	Reading—pages 43–50	7:00	Island of the Blue Dolphins
Tuesday	Spelling—write words in sentences	8:00	Spelling word list page 36
Wednesday	Math—top of page 142	6:30	Math Book Unit 10
Thursday	Social Studies—plan project with partner	3:30	Daniel Boone biography
Friday–Saturday	Art—finish Boonesborough	Saturday afternoon	Sticks, glue, brown paint

Day	Subject	Time	Materials

On another piece of paper, write the first stanza of this American folk song
in your best cursive handwriting.

This Land Is Your Land

This land is your land, this land is my land

From California to the New York island,

From the redwood forest to the Gulf Stream waters

This land was made for you and me.

As I was walking that ribbon of highway,

I saw above me that endless skyway,

I saw below me that golden valley

This land was made for you and me.

Woody Guthrie

Writing Quickly

Writing quickly is a skill that will help when you need to draft a story, write during a timed test, or take notes as your teacher talks. Writing that is done quickly should still be easy to read. With practice, you will learn how to make your writing speedy and legible.

Read the quotation below. Write it quickly and legibly in your best cursive handwriting. Be sure to leave space for margins.

"Remember that a journey of a thousand miles begins with a single step."

Write the saying again. Try to write it faster, but make sure your writing is legible. Leave room for margins.

Write the saying two more times. Try to write it even faster, but keep it easy to read and leave space for margins.

Now, read your final writing. Circle Yes or No to respond to each statement. Then show your writing to another reader, either a classmate or your teacher. Ask that person to circle Yes or No beside each statement.

	My Evaluation	My Classmate's or Teacher's Evaluation
The writing is easy to read.	Yes No	Yes No
The writing has good Shape.	Yes No	Yes No
The writing has good Size.	Yes No	Yes No
The writing has good Spacing.	Yes No	Yes No
The writing has good Slant.	Yes No	Yes No

Writing Easily

As you write stories and essays for school papers and tests, it is important that your handwriting flows easily. When you automatically know how to write legibly, you don't have to worry about your handwriting. You are free to think about what you want your writing to say. With practice, you will learn how to make your writing easy, quick, and legible.

Read the writing prompt below. Respond to it by writing in cursive on the lines. Let your handwriting flow easily as you think and write. Be sure to leave room for margins. Continue writing on the next page.

Persuasive Writing

Pretend you are running for president of your class.

Write a paragraph that will persuade your classmates to vote for you. Include details about what you would do as president and why you are a good candidate.

Now, read your final writing. Circle Yes or No to respond to each statement. Then show your writing to another reader, either a classmate or your teacher. Ask that person to circle Yes or No beside each statement.

	My Evaluation		My Classmate's or Teacher's Evaluation	
The writing is easy to read.	Yes	No	Yes	No
The writing has good Shape.	Yes	No	Yes	No
The writing has good Size.	Yes	No	Yes	No
The writing has good Spacing.	Yes	No	Yes	No
The writing has good Slant.	Yes	No	Yes	No

Handwriting and the Writing Process
Write a Paragraph

A paragraph is a group of sentences about a main idea.
Write a paragraph about your favorite holiday and how you celebrate it.

I. Prewriting
Prewriting means gathering ideas and planning before you write. List your ideas on a piece of paper. Then plan your paragraph. Write the subject and list the details that will support it.

2. Drafting
Drafting means writing your thoughts on paper. Use the subject and details you listed in Prewriting to draft your paragraph. Write your first draft. You do not have to use complete sentences. Just get your ideas down on paper.

3. Revising
Revising means changing your writing to make it say exactly what you mean. Write in complete sentences. Mark any changes you want to make.

Does your writing include all the information readers want to know?	Yes	No
Does your writing include descriptive details that support the subject or main idea?	Yes	No

4. Editing
Editing means checking your revised writing for errors in spelling, punctuation, capitalization, and handwriting.

Are all words spelled correctly?	Yes	No
Have you used uppercase letters and punctuation correctly?	Yes	No
Do your letters have good shape and size?	Yes	No
Is there good spacing between letters, words, and sentences?	Yes	No
Does your writing have good uniform slant?	Yes	No
Is your writing easy to read?	Yes	No

5. Publishing
Publishing means using your best handwriting to make an error-free copy of your writing. Share your writing.

Record of Student's Handwriting Skills
Cursive

	Needs Improvement	Shows Mastery
Sits correctly	☐	☐
Holds pencil correctly	☐	☐
Positions paper correctly	☐	☐
Writes numerals *1–10*	☐	☐
Writes undercurve letters: *i, t, u, w, e, l, b, h*	☐	☐
Writes undercurve letters: *f, k, r, s, j, p*	☐	☐
Writes downcurve letters: *a, d, g, o, c, q*	☐	☐
Writes overcurve letters: *n, m, y, x, v, z*	☐	☐
Writes downcurve letters: *A, O, D, C, E*	☐	☐
Writes curve forward letters: *N, M, H, K, U, Y, Z, V, W, X*	☐	☐
Writes overcurve letters: *I, J, Q*	☐	☐
Writes doublecurve letters: *T, F*	☐	☐
Writes undercurve-loop letters: *G, S, L*	☐	☐
Writes undercurve-slant letters: *P, R, B*	☐	☐
Writes the undercurve-to-undercurve joining	☐	☐
Writes the undercurve-to-downcurve joining	☐	☐
Writes the undercurve-to-overcurve joining	☐	☐
Writes the overcurve-to-undercurve joining	☐	☐
Writes the overcurve-to-downcurve joining	☐	☐
Writes the overcurve-to-overcurve joining	☐	☐
Writes the checkstroke-to-undercurve joining	☐	☐
Writes the checkstroke-to-downcurve joining	☐	☐
Writes the checkstroke-to-overcurve joining	☐	☐
Writes with correct shape	☐	☐
Writes with correct size	☐	☐
Writes with correct spacing	☐	☐
Writes with uniform slant	☐	☐
Writes quickly	☐	☐
Writes with ease	☐	☐
Regularly checks written work for legibility	☐	☐

Index